Gratitude Diary

by Gisela Ludman Rojzman

How could I dare?

This adventure started a while ago. I was always writing down my dreams, tears, comments, and ideas, and I kept them stashed away on different little sheets of papers. But it never occured to me that the day would come when I would decide to share these with the world. **How could I dare...?**

Let me introduce myself. I am not a writer, a public speaker, a motivator, an extrovert or introvert. I am somewhere in the middle, at least for now. I am a mother, wife and rabbi's wife, sister, daughter, niece, cousin and friend. A meditator, a responsible patient to all my doctors, a lazy exerciser, a listener, a brutally honest person with myself, an overthinker, a volunteer, an immigrant, a lover of flowers and plants, someone committed to harmony and order, and an expert at cooking my squash chicken soup. This I learned from my mom. I am someone who has consistently chosen psychotherapy for over 30 years as a way of life, I am always trying to be non-judgemental, and I am moldable. I am also or, more accurately, used to be a practicing Argentinian lawyer, having graduated from The University of Buenos Aires a million years ago. I am now a Marriage and Family Therapist in Miami, Florida since graduating from Nova Southeastern University in 2007.

As a therapist, I am constantly looking for new ways to help my consultants achieve their goals, take charge of their lives, avoid denial, and live with more serenity by instilling the attitude of gratitude in their lives.
Even though I do not practice law anymore, I still often think like a lawyer. So, I propose that you sign onto the following bilateral contract between *YOU*, the reader and journaler-writer-to-be, and *ME*, the one hoping to share this *gift*. Your only mandatory task is that you give it a try. My job is to offer this life changing tool to you.

ME Signature

YOU Signature

Goals of this diary

A shaman I met years ago taught me the importance of clearly knowing one's intentions. And she was so right.

My two intentions for this journey with you are:

I. Return to handwriting

Our script is like a second fingerprint. Each is unique, different, and our own. However, it is a trait that we have begun, without realizing, to erase as we use our phones and computers instead. This is a pity. We don't use hand notes anymore - our supermarket lists, our calendars, and everyone's contact information is all on our phones. I still remember the first sentence I wrote in first grade. "Mi mama me ama," "My mom loves me."

Do you remember the first sentence you ever wrote...?

This diary will not have a corrector or spellcheck. It will be a private encounter with yourself, the pen or pencil you use, and your own decision to **cultivate a new culture of gratitude** in your life. I challenge you to close your eyes and picture the handwriting of your parents or grandparents for example. **Did you do it...?** Maybe you can envision it, maybe it even brought back intense emotions, maybe it made you as weirdly proud to remember as it does to me. *The goal is to bring back this fingerprint. It is a way of making sure that our children will know our handwriting and that we will know theirs.*

II. Encounter gratitude

Encountering gratitude has been one of the most valuable discoveries of my life. As Cicero said, *"Gratitude is not only the greatest of virtues, but the parent of all others."* I have come to understand that no problem affects my whole life, though it may often seem all-encompassing. I understand that my daily loving kindness meditation and my journaling about gratitude are healthy ways to connect with the present moment. Expressing gratitude helps bring you to the here and now. I challenge you to rethink gratitude as a verb which pushes you to find new ways of feeling thankful, showing appreciation, and returning kindness.

I always tell my consultants that, while they are the experts of their own lives, tools are needed to help us remember which paths to take and which to steer clear of, what good love looks like, and which relationships to avoid. Connecting with the present can serve as a channel toward completeness, wholeness, and satisfaction in life. Recording my blessings has served as a daily reminder for me that, though I am often distracted, the simple things in life are what makes one most content.

Pain exists and is part of our journeys. Complications, storms, illnesses, regrets, losses, failures, ups and downs, and accidents are all a part of life. All of us have been affected by pain, stress, and disappointment. Nobody leaves this world unscratch. When we work on acceptance and gratitude, the struggle ends and we embrace clarity and calmness. The bad news is that pain never ends. *The good news is that cultivating an attitude of gratitude can help you overcome the suffering.* The pain may still be there, but suffering becomes a choice. If you commit to this process, peace and serenity may accompany your days.

A few ideas on how to use this diary:

I learned from Gillian Deacon, that "*there is no prescription for finding moments of gratitude in every day: there is simply **the choice**.*"
In this workbook, you will find pages to write about that which you are thankful for daily. There is no correct way to do it. You can write one word, one sentence, or as many as you desire as long as you are using it as a medium through which to pay attention to the blessings in your life.

About the quotes you will read...

On each page, you will find a quote which has inspired me over the years. I learn from Julio Cortazar that "in quoting others, we cite ourselves." The quotes that you will read have been talking to me in different ways for years. I hope they will also speak to you. They are about life, pleasure, pain, gain, loss, and gratitude. I learn from them, I internalize them, and I try to apply them to my life. You may or may not feel the same way, but I only ask that you give them a try!

Now, it's time for your exploration.

And one last tip...
My good days always begin with gratitude. I hope that yours will too!

"A good deed leads to another good deed" - Pirkei Avot 4:2

I am grateful for... Date: 6/11/19

family
doctors
friends
food

"Let us be grateful to people who make us happy, they are the charming gardeners who make our souls blossom" - Marcel Proust

I am grateful for... Date:

"You are free, and that is why you are lost" - Franz Kafka

I am grateful for... Date:

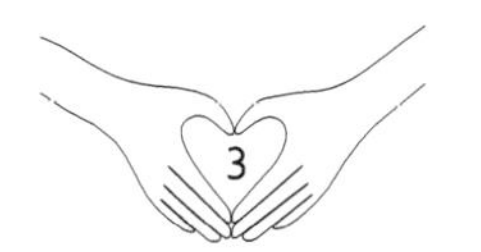

"Commitment is an act, not a word" - Jean Paul Sartre

I am grateful for... Date:

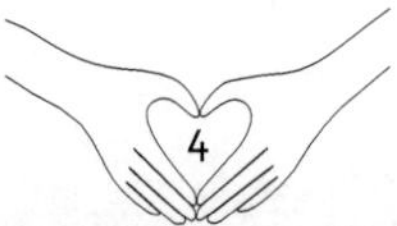

"The present moment is all you ever have" - Eckhart Tolle

I am grateful for... Date:

"Be careful of your own sensibility" - Monica Dalin

I am grateful for... Date:

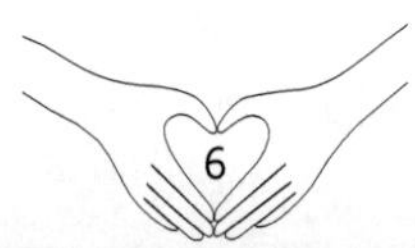

"Have a clear intention" - Maria Munay Machi

I am grateful for... Date:

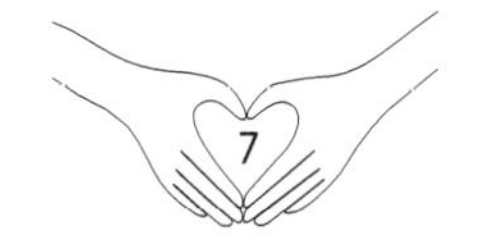

"Ring the bells that still can ring. Forget your perfect offering. There is a crack in everything. That is how the light gets in" - Leonard Cohen

I am grateful for... Date:

"Be kind whenever possible. It is always possible" - Dalai Lama

I am grateful for... Date:

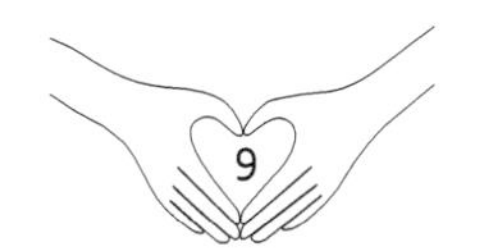

"Freedom is what you do with what's been done to you" - Jean Paul Sartre

I am grateful for... Date:

"Kindness is the language which the deaf can hear and the blind can see" - Mark Twain

I am grateful for... Date:

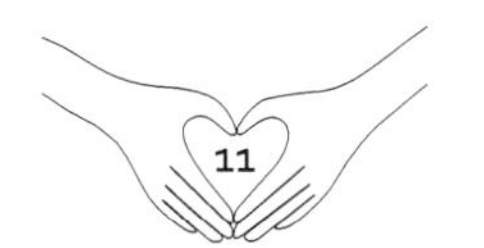

"Taking a new step, uttering a new word, is what people fear most" - Fyodor Dostoyevsky

I am grateful for... Date:

"The voyage of discovery is not in seeking new landscapes but in having new eyes" - Marcel Proust

I am grateful for... Date:

"Gratitude is a two way flow of appreciation between your thanks and the uplifting response that you feel in return" - Deepak Chopra

I am grateful for... Date:

"Human beings evolve through try and error. We accumulate data, we have theories, and we prove them even if they are not right"- Andres Oppenheimer

I am grateful for... Date:

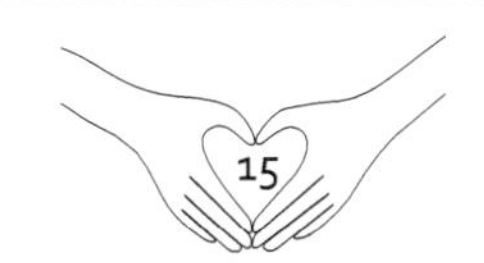

"If we practice one random act of kindness a day, we will have practiced 365 kind acts that year"
- Shelly Tygielski

I am grateful for... Date:

"Life is a good teacher and a good friend" - Pema Chodron

I am grateful for... Date:

"Fake it until you make it. Fake it until you become it" - Amy Cuddy

I am grateful for... Date:

"People do not really want freedom, because freedom involves responsibility, and most people are frightened of responsibility" - Sigmund Freud

I am grateful for... Date:

"There are three categories of people, givers, takers, and matchers" - Adam Grant

I am grateful for... Date:

"The only normal people are the ones you don't know very well" - Alfred Adler

I am grateful for... Date:

"The privilege of a lifetime is being who you are" - Joseph Campbell

I am grateful for... Date:

"There is nothing more life changing than gratitude" - Oprah Winfrey

I am grateful for... Date:

"Surrender to what is" - Eckhart Tolle

I am grateful for... Date:

"Grace is not knowledge or reason. Grace is the amount of light in our souls" - Pope Francis

I am grateful for... Date:

"True wisdom is being able to say it is what it is with a smile of celebratory wonder on your face"
- Eric Micha'el Leventhal

I am grateful for... Date:

"There is always another way to get where you are going" - Gillian Deacon

I am grateful for... Date:

"Giving up hope of getting ground under our feet" - Pema Chodron

I am grateful for... Date:

"Peace is our gift to each other" - Elie Wiesel

I am grateful for... Date:

"Sooner or later people need to give up the hope of a better past" - Irvin Yalom

I am grateful for... Date:

"Core relationships also change. From unconditionality, they change to reciprocity" - Monica Dalin

I am grateful for... Date:

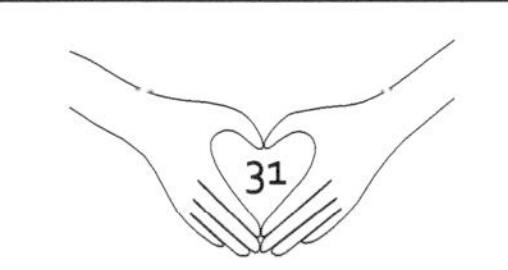

"When we are no longer able to change a situation, we are challenged to change ourselves"
- Viktor E. Frankl

I am grateful for... Date:

"One looks back with appreciation to the brilliant teachers, but with gratitude to those who touched our human feelings" - Carl Jung

I am grateful for... Date:

"The use of language pacifies" - Jacques Lacan

I am grateful for... Date:

"The big things can only be created together" - Mario Kreutzberger

I am grateful for... Date:

"There is only one day left, always starting over: it is given to us at dawn and taken away from us at dusk" - Jean Paul Sartre

I am grateful for... Date:

"Four Agreements: Do not make assumptions, Do not take things personally. Always do your best. Be impeccable with your words" - Don Miguel Ruiz

I am grateful for... Date:

"When a person doesn't have gratitude, something is missing in his or her humanity" - Elie Wiesel

I am grateful for... Date:

"Who looks outside, dreams, who looks inside, awakes" - Carl Jung

I am grateful for... Date:

"For the meaning of life differs from man to man, from day to day and from hour to hour. What matters, therefore, is not the meaning of life in general, but rather the specific meaning of a person's life at a given moment" - Viktor E. Frankl

I am grateful for... Date:

"Always say yes to the present moment" - Eckhart Tolle

I am grateful for... Date:

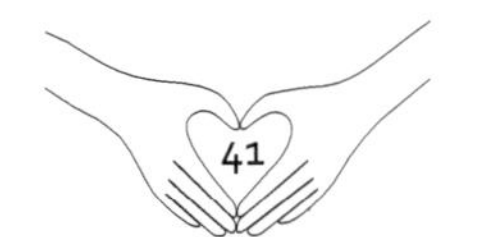

"Don't talk unless you can improve the silence" - Jorge Luis Borges

I am grateful for... Date:

"For what you do to others, you do to yourself"- Eckhart Tolle

I am grateful for... Date:

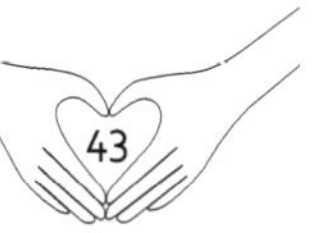

"A human being is a deciding being" - Viktor E. Frankl

I am grateful for... Date:

"Lose your mind and come to your senses" - Fritz Perls

I am grateful for... Date:

"Trade your expectation for appreciation and the world changes instantly" - Tony Robbins

I am grateful for... Date:

"Look inside you and be strong. And you will finally see the truth that a hero lies in you"
- Mariah Carey

I am grateful for... Date:

"Educating the mind without educating the heart is no education at all" - Aristotle

I am grateful for...   Date:

"There is always gonna be another mountain, I'm always gonna wanna make it move" - Miley Cyrus

I am grateful for... Date:

"People do not need good things or events in order to feel gratitude. Grateful people reframe whatever happens to them" - Dr. Robert Emmons

I am grateful for... Date:

"We are our memory, we are the chimerical museum of shifting shapes, that pile of broken mirrors"
- Jorge Luis Borges

I am grateful for... Date:

"Good actions give strength to ourselves and inspire good actions in others" - Plato

I am grateful for... Date:

"It is not true that people stop pursuing dreams because they grow old, they grow old because they stop pursuing dreams" - Gabriel Garcia Marquez

I am grateful for... Date:

"I am my own muse, I am the subject I know best. The subject I want to know better" - Frida Kahlo

I am grateful for... Date:

"Happiness is when what you think, what you say, and what you do are in harmony"
- Mahatma Gandhi

I am grateful for... Date:

"Kind words can be short and easy to speak, but their echoes are truly endless" - Mother Teresa

I am grateful for... Date:

"I have decided to stick with love. Hate is too great a burden to bear" - Martin Luther King Jr.

I am grateful for... Date:

"The more grateful we are, the more connected we become to the universe around us"
- Stephen Richards

I am grateful for... Date:

"It is in your moments of decision that your destiny is shaped" - Tony Robbins

I am grateful for... Date:

"I don't accumulate things" - Marcos Aguinis

I am grateful for... Date:

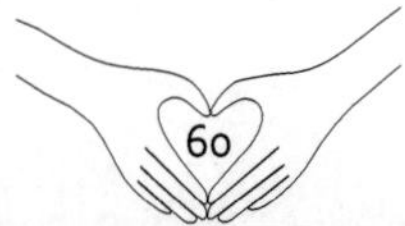

"If nothing saves us from death, at least love should save us from life" - Pablo Neruda

I am grateful for... Date:

"If you judge people, you have no time to love them" - Mother Teresa

I am grateful for... Date:

"The time is always right to do what is right" - Martin Luther King Jr.

I am grateful for... Date:

"The superficial changes. The depth changes. The way of thinking changes" - Everything changes in this world - Mercedes Sosa

I am grateful for... Date:

"Spirituality is seeded, germinates, sprouts and blossoms in the mundane. It is to be found and nurtured in the smallest of daily activities" - Thomas Moore

I am grateful for... Date:

"Surrender means wisely accommodating ourselves to what is beyond our control" - Sylvia Boorstein

I am grateful for... Date:

"Human freedom involves our capacity to pause between the stimulus and response and, in that pause, to choose the one response toward which we wish to throw our weight" - Rollo May

I am grateful for... Date:

"Beginnings are usually scary, and endings are usually sad, but it is everything in between what makes it all worth living" - Bob Marley

I am grateful for... Date:

"How lucky I am to have something that makes saying goodbye so hard" - Winnie the Pooh

I am grateful for...   Date:

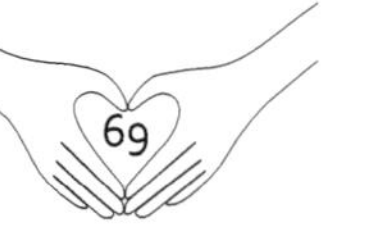

"There is no right way to do a wrong thing" - Rabbi Harold Kushner

I am grateful for... Date:

Remember to use your five senses

I am grateful for... Date:

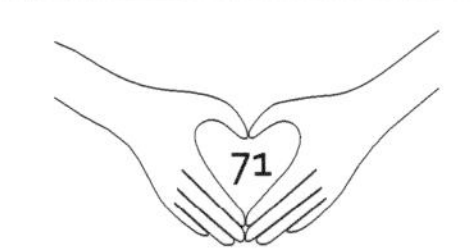

"Write what should not be forgotten" - Isabel Allende

I am grateful for... Date:

"Laws of nature do not make exceptions for nice people" - Rabbi Harold Kushner

I am grateful for... Date:

"Life is not what is supposed to be. It is what it is. The way you cope with it is what makes the difference" - Virginia Satir

I am grateful for... Date:

"You are the storyteller of your own life and you can create your own legend or not"- Isabel Allende

I am grateful for... Date:

"My pain may be the reason for somebody's laugh. But my laugh must never be a reason for some-body's pain" - Charlie Chaplin

I am grateful for... Date:

"There are only two ways to live your life. One is as though nothing is a miracle. The other is as though everything is a miracle" - Albert Einstein

I am grateful for... Date:

"I can shake off everything as I write; my sorrows disappear, my courage is reborn" - Anne Frank

I am grateful for... Date:

"Take care of the words you use. There are people who listen with their heart" - Ona Daurada

I am grateful for... Date:

"When you ask yourself why me? Respond to yourself, why not me?" - Mindy Kaling

I am grateful for... Date:

"Tolerate, accept, then embrace" - Neal Pollard

I am grateful for... Date:

"Hold the door, say please say thank you. Do not steal, do not cheat, do not lie. I know you got mountains to climb but always stay humble and kind" - Tim McGraw

I am grateful for... Date:

"He who has a why to live for can bear almost any how" - Viktor Frankl

I am grateful for... Date:

"If I am not for me, who is for me, and if I am only for myself, what am I. And if not now, when"
- Hillel

I am grateful for... Date:

"A man doesn't have time in his life to have time for everything. He doesn't have seasons enough to have a season for every purpose" - Yehuda Amichai

I am grateful for... Date:

"Keep my tongue from evil and my lips free from speaking lies" - Psalm 34:13

I am grateful for... Date:

"From so much loss, I learn to win" - Jorge Luis Borges

I am grateful for... Date:

"When life shows you a thousand reasons to cry, show that you have a thousand and one reasons to smile" - Facundo Cabral

I am grateful for... Date:

"I think that life is a good book, the further you get into it, the more it begins to make sense"
- Rabbi Harold Kushner

I am grateful for... Date:

"Whoever is happy will make others happy too" - Anne Frank

I am grateful for... Date:

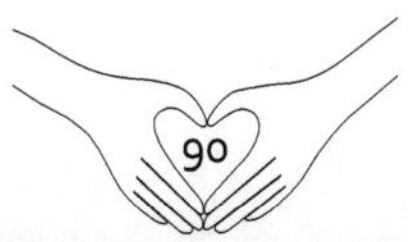

Sincere gratitude:

To my quiet mornings and meditations, my walks, dinners with friends and family, scented candles, rainy days, sunny days, a good movie, music, a hug, a good book, the noise, the silence, chocolate, a sweet nap, a long bath.

To my parents, who when I was a child were very strict in instructing me to always say THANK YOU. During those days, I learned it the hard way. I had to thank, and to thank, and to thank, or I would be in real trouble. I guess I learned the lesson. Thank you for this teaching. The house I grew up in is full of frames with pictures of every family member and phrases they recollected over the years. Nowadays, my house is full of pictures, and my heart is full of the inspirational phrases I shared with you. Thank you for being the original inspiration.

To my husband, the love of my life, the one who makes me laugh every single day and who always makes my life less complicated. His choosing me everyday gives me the strength to always keep on going.

To my teachers, my children:
To Henri, the oldest, the one who grew up alongside me. Through him I learned to greater appreciate the values of perseverance and endurance.
To Sarit, the one who was physically far. Through her I learned to greater appreciate the values of autonomy and vivacity.
To Igal, the one who had to keep up with my feelings of unconditional love. Through him I learned to greater appreciate the values of generosity and sensibility .
To Danu, the one who had to keep up with many of my fears. Through her I learned to greater appreciate the values of honesty, courage, and solidity.
To Annie, the youngest, the one who has been keeping up with my desperation of love and care. Through her I learned to greater appreciate the values of kind-heartedness and resilience.

To my siblings: I always loved the concept that the relationship with your brothers and sisters is supposed to be the longest one. Through them I learned to greater appreciate the value of mutual trust.

To my Uncles and Aunts, with capital letters, for their continuous and huge love throughout my life.
To Monica, who has been there all the way and more.
To Silvi Z"L, for her eternal and unique smile.
To the friends who have kept me motivated to work on this workbook, telling me things like *this project is really YOU.*
To Vero Zalcberg the best designer, thank you.

Farewell:

Years ago, I learned the concept of the ladder to sanctity from my husband. He explained to me that a spiritual journey can be illustrated with an imaginary staircase. It is a staircase that never ends and each person can dwell in each step as long as he or she needs. Practicing gratitude has allowed me to take an extra step in that ladder and to find more calmness, completeness, awareness and the gift of living in the present.

Gisela

P.S.: I would love to hear from you. Please write to me at gratitudediarybygisela@gmail.com

NOTES

NOTES

NOTES

Made in the USA
Columbia, SC
03 June 2019